MORE

BRILLIANT
ADVICE!

by Annie Lawson

A Deirdre McDonald Book

BELLEW PUBLISHING

London

First published in 1989
by Deirdre McDonald Books
Bellew Publishing Co. Ltd.
7 Southampton Place, London WC1A 2DR

ISBN 0 947792 24 4

Printed in Hong Kong by
Regent Publishing Services Ltd

brown rice!
OH NO!
muesli!
YERK!
kaftans!
lentil stew!
YIK!
tahini!
Donovan!
painted vans!
OW!
breastfeeding!
RETCH!
just a minute... we believe in that

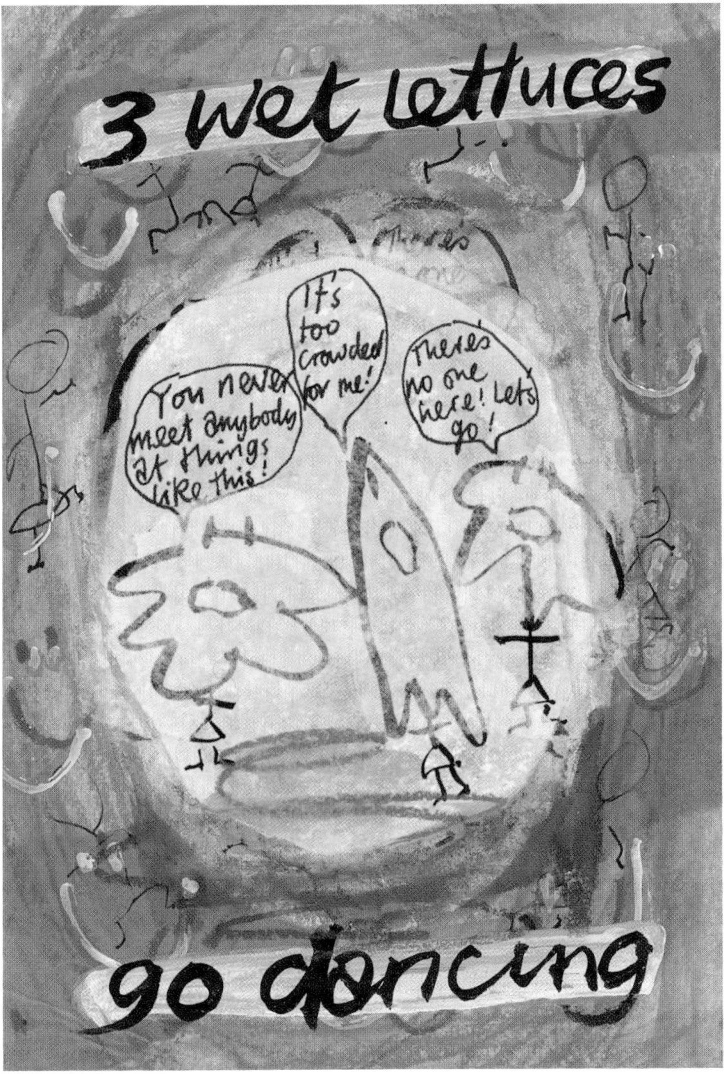
3 wet lettuces
You never meet anybody at things like this!
It's too crowded for me!
Theres no one here! Lets go!
go dancing

Clubbing It

IT'S HARD TO LOOK COOL
WITH A PIECE OF BOGROLL
STUCK TO YOUR FOOT.

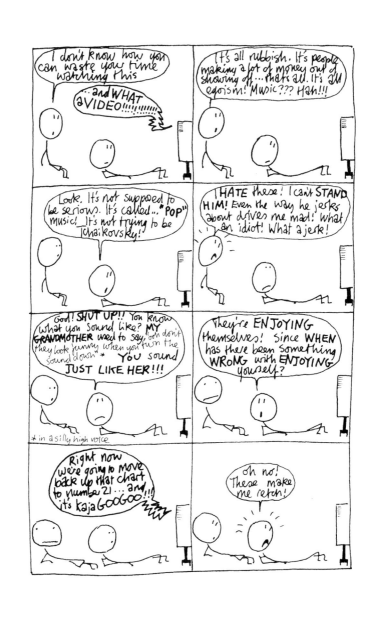

Jane sometimes listens to WINNIE TAMMETTE ...
I always have a good laugh at this!
WINNIE TAM-METTE
Today a posse of women came to see me... ♪
...To make me realise women don't have equal rights. But they went when I told them... I feel equal ...to an angel... ♪
...when my man holds me at night... ♪
My man he treats me like a baby And he's so gentle and so nice to me ,....♪
What's this crap?
Shut up Simon!
So I do all I can to please him... cos my man works hard & takes good care of me....♪
God... This is TERRIBLE!
DON'T LIB-ER-ATE ME... JUST LOVE ME... ♪
How can you CALL YOURSELF A FEMINIST AND LISTEN TO THIS RUBBISH?!
Cos I'm as free as I'll ever want to be. Some women just cain't understand ...there's quite a lot of difference...♪
It's fantasy
What? You want to be like THAT?!
between a woman and a man... And I just know that's the way God meant it to be...♪
NO!
SOME women take this SERIOUSLY!...
So love me and don't lib-er-ate me...♪
...in MILTON KEYNES!
oh fuck off!

IT'S THE FASHIONABLE THING NOWADAYS FOR OLDER WOMEN TO GO OUT WITH YOUNGER MEN, FOR:-
CHINESE BURNS
DEAD-LEGS
"HORSEBITES"
PARALYSING NECK-GRIPS
...OR THE EMOTIONAL EQUIVALENTS

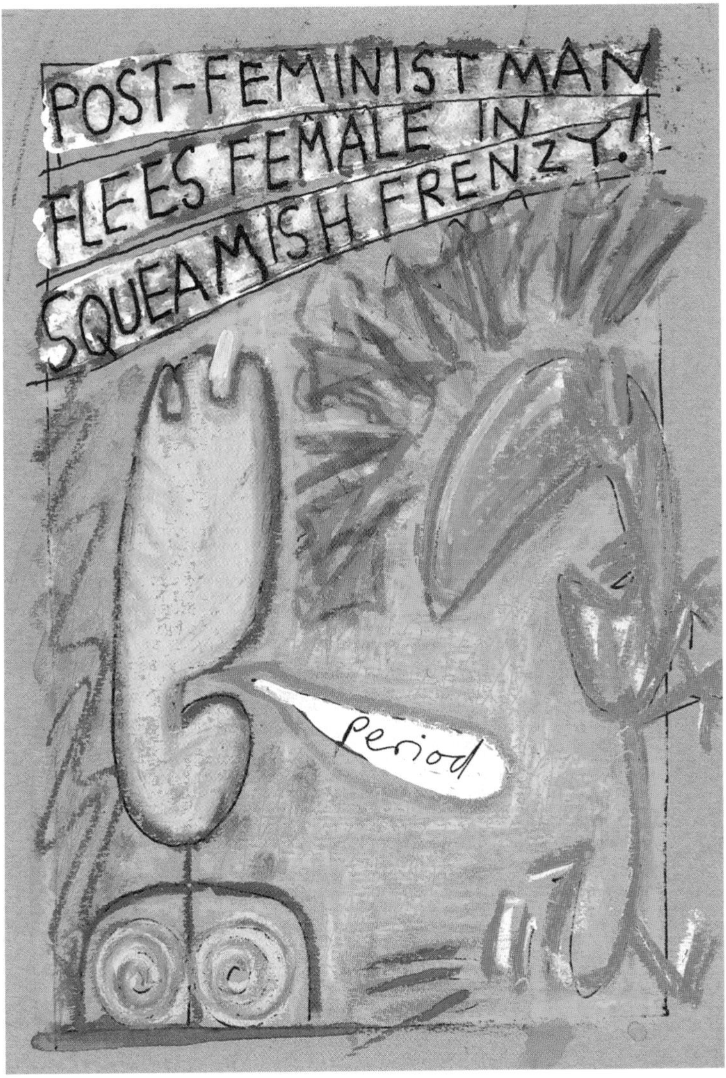
POST-FEMINIST MAN
FLEES FEMALE IN
SQUEAMISH FRENZY.!
Period

GLOOM
Something has to happen soon. I CAN'T GO ON!
I hate my work
...and RELATIONSHIPS? SCREAM! DON'T MAKE ME LAUGH!
SELF PITY
AH! Time for "DALLAS"!
Sue Ellen, your marriage to J.R. is desparately unhappy. Why don't you quit?
No Jenna! I've somehow coped up to now! Maybe I'll try separate bedrooms
HAPPY
...but there's some-thing missing...
THERE'S THIS GREAT HOLLOW IN MY LIFE...

Assertiveness Training

I WOULDN'T EVEN GIVE HIM THE STEAM FROM MY PISS!

TOM was at his girlfriend's, JULIA had an important meeting, and HELEN had stopped in the previous week for the gas people. So when NELSON had his EYE, it was down to IAN to take him to the vet...
I STILL say HELEN should have! she's got a CAR for god's sake!
TEAR! RATTLE!
KARRY-PET BOX
SCRABBLE!
WAITING ROOM
What have you got in there? A kitten?
Yes. It's only got one eye! It had an abcess behind the other and scratched it out at birth. Now it's gone septic!
SICK
GREEN
Oh... poor little thing! Best have it put down eh?
KARRY-PET BOX
MIEOW!
Hmf! Maybe!
...and TOM should make his mind up where he's living!... I may be un-employed but I've still got THINGS TO DO! It wasn't MY decision to get a cat! JULIA! It's JULIA's responsibility! But JULIA is at a MEETING! "Let's RESCUE the poor little ONE-EYED RUNT," she goes! The bloody thing will be RUNNING ROUND IN CIRCLES...
KARRY-PET BOX
But... will it be able to lead a normal life, vet?
Oh yes! I'll give him a course of antibiotics to clear up the infection and he'll be as right as rain!
PLEASED AS A CAT WITH 2 TAILS

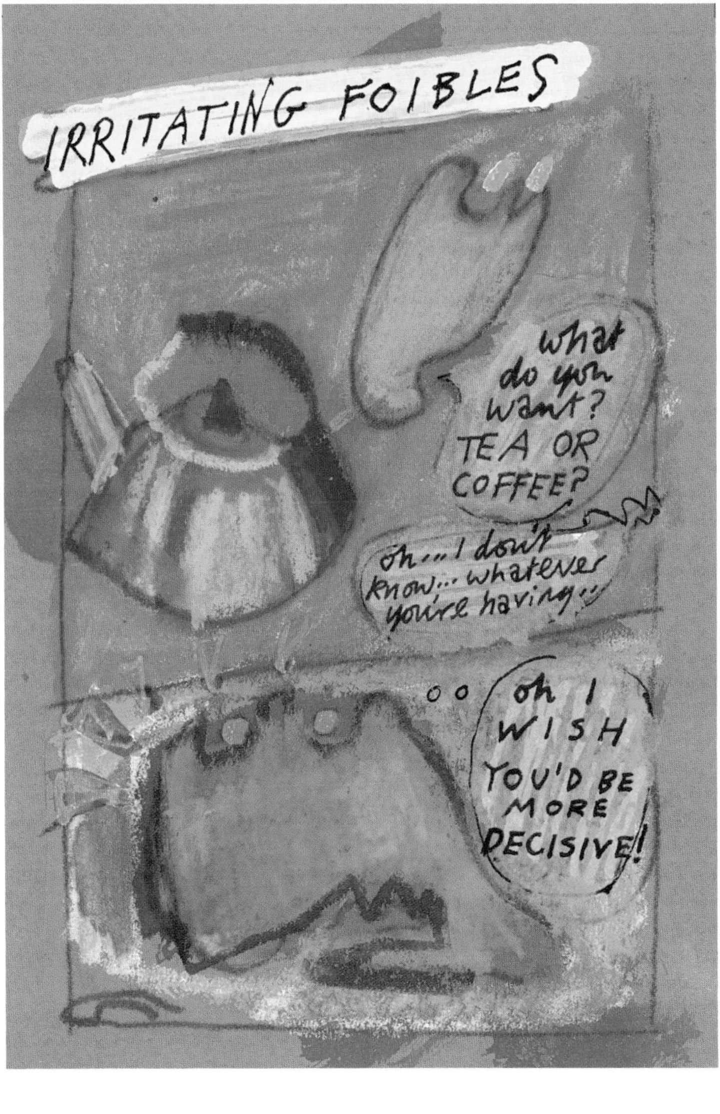
IRRITATING FOIBLES
what do you want? TEA OR COFFEE?
oh... I don't know... whatever you're having...
oh I WISH YOU'D BE MORE DECISIVE!

What do you think of that SADE? Do you really think she's as brilliant as they say?
For the 25th time Gillian, it's SHAR-DAY!!!

Honestly Alison, I'm continually flabbergasted at your total lack of knowledge! You're the most POLITICALLY IGNORANT person I know!
I bet you don't even know who NEIL KINNOCK is! Come on... who's Neil Kinnock?
That's not fair! I AM political..
...I HATE THE QUEEN!!!
Alison... you hate THE QUEEN because you don't like her HAIRSTYLE! Come on... WHO'S NEIL KINNOCK?
I don't hate the queen's hairstyle! I HATE PRINCESS DI'S HAIRSTYLE!!!
It's no reason not to like someone just because you don't like their HAIR-STYLE ALISON!
God, you're so shallow! How can I know you? It's embarrassing!
Anyway... I do know who Neil Kinnock is.. he's someone in the government!
oh WELL DONE! 10 out of 10!!!!!!
CLAP
I made an interesting observation the other day Alison.. Have you noticed that Princess Di's hairstyle is the same as that bloke's in WHAM?
What's Wham?

Do you think SIMON will be at Sonia's party?
I don't know...
I have to face it! I'm forced to bump into him sooner or later so there's no point in hiding round corners!
otherwise he'd still be ruling my life wouldn't he? If he says, "Hello! Long time no see!" I'LL say, "NOT LONG ENOUGH, YOU CREEP!"
...or I might say... "If it wasn't such a timeworn cliché you'd get this drink in your face PAL!!"
that's good!
or... "As far as I'M concerned, Simon, YOU'RE DEAD. So please remove your DEAD BODY from where I'm standing!" Hey... that's good!
No, come to think of it I won't say anything! I'll just STARE THROUGH him as if he's invisible! That's the best don't you think?
um...
Later.. at SONIA'S PARTY...
HE'S NOT HERE!! I had this whole speech worked out!
Well, as far as I know he doesn't know Sonia does he?

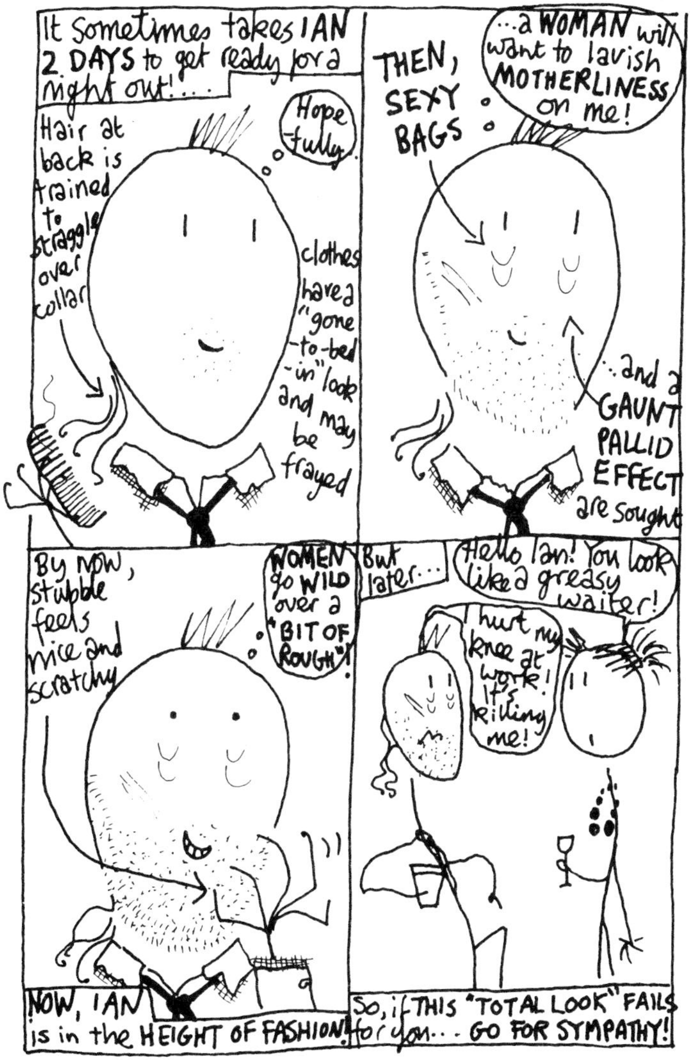

It sometimes takes IAN 2 DAYS to get ready for a night out!...
Hair at back is trained to straggle over collar
Hope-fully.
clothes have a "gone-to-bed-in" look and may be frayed
THEN, SEXY BAGS
...a WOMAN will want to lavish MOTHERLINESS on me!
...and a GAUNT PALLID EFFECT are sought
By now, stubble feels nice and scratchy
WOMEN go WILD over a "BIT OF ROUGH"!
NOW, IAN is in the HEIGHT OF FASHION!
But later...
Hello Ian! You look like a greasy waiter!
I hurt my knee at work! It's killing me!
So, if THIS "TOTAL LOOK" FAILS for you... GO FOR SYMPATHY!

I'm rather glad celibacy is fashionable nowadays

THE DAY BEFORE SUSIE LEFT HE SAT IN THE BATH + LOOKED AT ALL THE COSMETIC BOTTLES, TOMORROW THEY WOULD BE GONE!

IT'S A GENERAL RULE THAT MEN FIND IT HARD TO OPEN UP TO OTHER MEN ABOUT PERSONAL PROBLEMS. WHY IS THIS?
This is MICHAEL. He's in the wars! He has SEXUALLY TRANSMITTED WARTS. Observe what happens when he confides this to a set of pals...
I've got warts on my dick!
HA HA HA!
hoo hoo!
HARRR!
...whereas a WOMAN with it, confiding in her WOMEN FRIENDS...
oh! POOR YOU!
oh NO! That's TERRIBLE!!
poor you!
Did WHATSIT give them to you? The FUCKING BASTARD!
Another example is PAUL...
MY problem is that a FUNDAMENTAL RELATIONSHIP in my life is in its FINAL DEATH THROES. I have many women confidantes, but still feel the need to talk to some-one the same sex as myself...
...I don't have any what you might call "CLOSE" men friends, but for SUPPORT I finally turned to NICK
NICK... we must talk! A FUNDA-MENTAL RELATIONSHIP in my life is in its FINAL DEATH THROES!
Well Paul, I must say I'm glad you're opening up like this...
...because there are TRAUMATIC PERSONAL HAPPEN-INGS in MY life at this point in time also! MY PRIMARY SEX CONTACT is having a scene with this bloke at work and... drone blah... bore
CAN'T GET A WORD IN EDGEWAYS FOR 3 HRS.

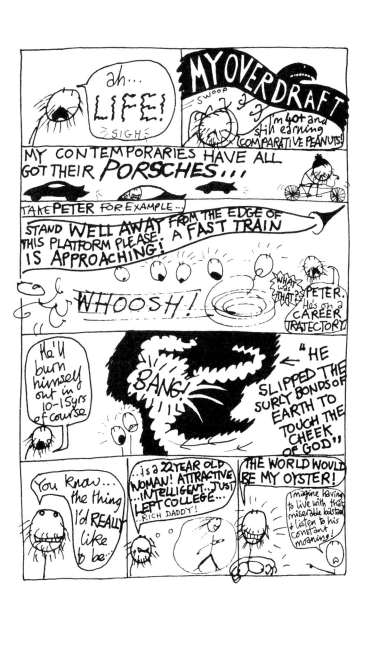

KETTLE'S FUCKED

WET LETTUCE
I'm feeling down
I wonder why?
maybe it's the crappy weather
or maybe it's that I'm not living with a wildly attractive intellectually stimulating wise caring EROTIC human being who makes me laugh 100% of the time...
...and who doesn't invade my space.
WAIL
YEAH
MUSING

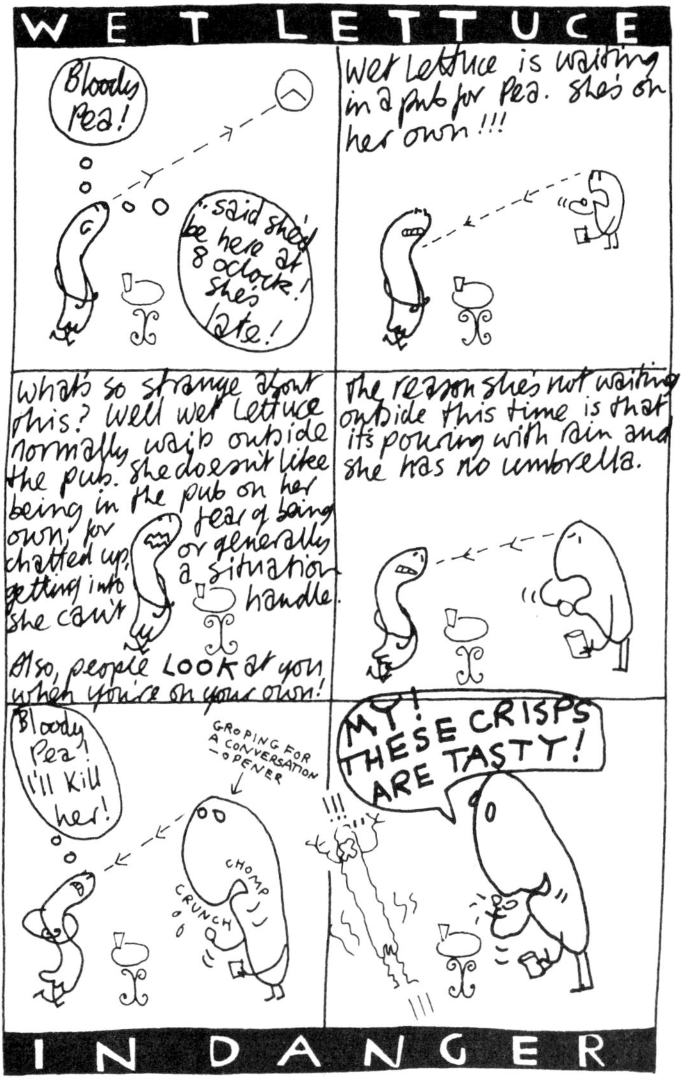
WET LETTUCE
Bloody Pea!
...said she'd be here at 8 o'clock! She's late!
Wet Lettuce is waiting in a pub for Pea. She's on her own!!!
What's so strange about this? Well Wet Lettuce normally waits outside the pub. She doesn't like being in the pub on her own, for fear of being chatted up, or generally getting into a situation she can't handle.
Also, people LOOK at you when you're on your own!
The reason she's not waiting outside this time is that it's pouring with rain and she has no umbrella.
Bloody Pea! I'll kill her!
GROPING FOR A CONVERSATION OPENER
CHOMP
CRUNCH
MY! THESE CRISPS ARE TASTY!
IN DANGER

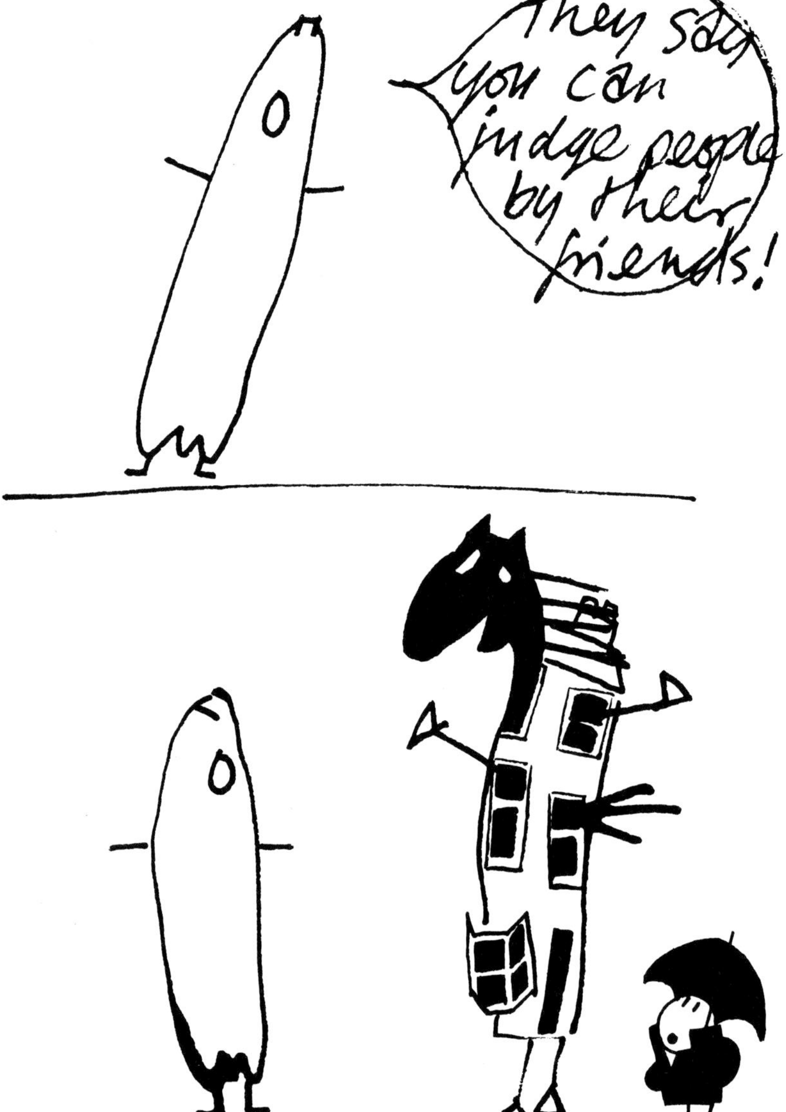
They said you can judge people by their friends!